Bark in the Park!

Poems for Dog Lovers

Cocker Spaniel

Boxer

Bloodhound

Bull Terrier

Rottweiler

Bedlington Terrier

Weimaraner

Dachshund

German Shepherd

Doberman Pinscher

Bark in the Park!

Poems for Dog Lovers

BY Avery Corman   PICTURES BY Hyewon Yum

SCHOLASTIC INC.

For James and Sebastian
—A.C.

For Sam and Sahn
—H.Y.

Afghan Hound

Although he's noble and aloof,
He's still a dog, so he still says, "Woof!"

Basset Hound

For things she can smell,
She's a comer and goer.
She's much like a Beagle,
But longer and lower.

Beagle
The Beagle is bent
On tracking a scent.
He follows his nose
Wherever it goes.

Bloodhound

If someone has to be found,
You needn't have a doubt.
The Bloodhound, nose to the ground,
Is going to find him out.

Boxer

The Boxer used to like to fight,
But nowadays she's more polite.

Bulldog

The Bulldog is lumpy
And always looks grumpy.
He's sweet, though, not cruel.
He does like to drool.

Pug

Is the Pug cute
Or is the Pug ugh?
Mostly, people love
The little Pug's mug.

Great Dane

She's taller than tall
When you stand beside her.
Why, she's so tall,
You can almost ride her.

Chihuahua
Super frisky, never whiny,
Even though he's teeny tiny.

Dachshund
She's a happy, little squat dog
Who looks like she's a hot dog.

Weimaraner

He's sleek and smooth, silvery gray,
An easy dog to tell.
But his name is hard to say
And harder still to spell.

Cocker Spaniel
She's an always on-the-run dog,
A floppy ears and fun dog.

Bedlington Terrier

The Bedlington Terrier
Couldn't be merrier.
A really nice dog to keep,
Who feels like and looks like a sheep.

Bull Terrier

A scrappy guy with lots of hustle,
He's one part dog and one part muscle.

Smooth Fox Terrier

As foxy as the fox is foxy,
It takes a dog with lots of moxie
To search among the fields and rocks
And then outfox the foxy fox.

Jack Russell Terrier

She's going to catch any ball you toss her.
The Russell fetches like a whiz.
She doesn't like any dog to boss her.
She thinks she's bigger than she is.

German Shepherd

He's a police dog for some
Because he's so clever,
And a most loyal chum
Forever and ever.

Doberman Pinscher

She'll never flinch and it's a cinch,
The Pinscher's not a dog to pinch.

Rottweiler

He's really playful, which he shows you,
But that's mostly if he knows you.
You wouldn't want to steal his bone,
Or anything else that he may own.

Labrador Retriever

Whatever you lose, you'd better believe it,
The Labrador Retriever is sure to retrieve it.

Newfoundland

She always gives the water
A good battle.
Of course, she always uses
The dog paddle.

Poodle

The Poodle is quick to learn a trick.
You might say a Poodle can use her noodle.

Puli

She's a softy, not a bully,
And she's also fully woolly.

Old English Sheepdog

He's friendly and he's lovable,
And pushable and shoveable.

Greyhound

She's not an easy dog to chase
Because she'll beat you in a race.

Saluki

His speed can compare with a Greyhound,
But his face is a little kookier.
He has more hair than a Greyhound
And that makes him Saluki-er.

Border Collie

Working hard suits her fine.
She makes sheep stay in line.
Not an easy job, you see,
But she's as smart as a dog can be.

Collie

The Collie is known for his lovely coat
And for roaming where it's grassy.
A famous Collie, we should note,
Once had the name of Lassie.

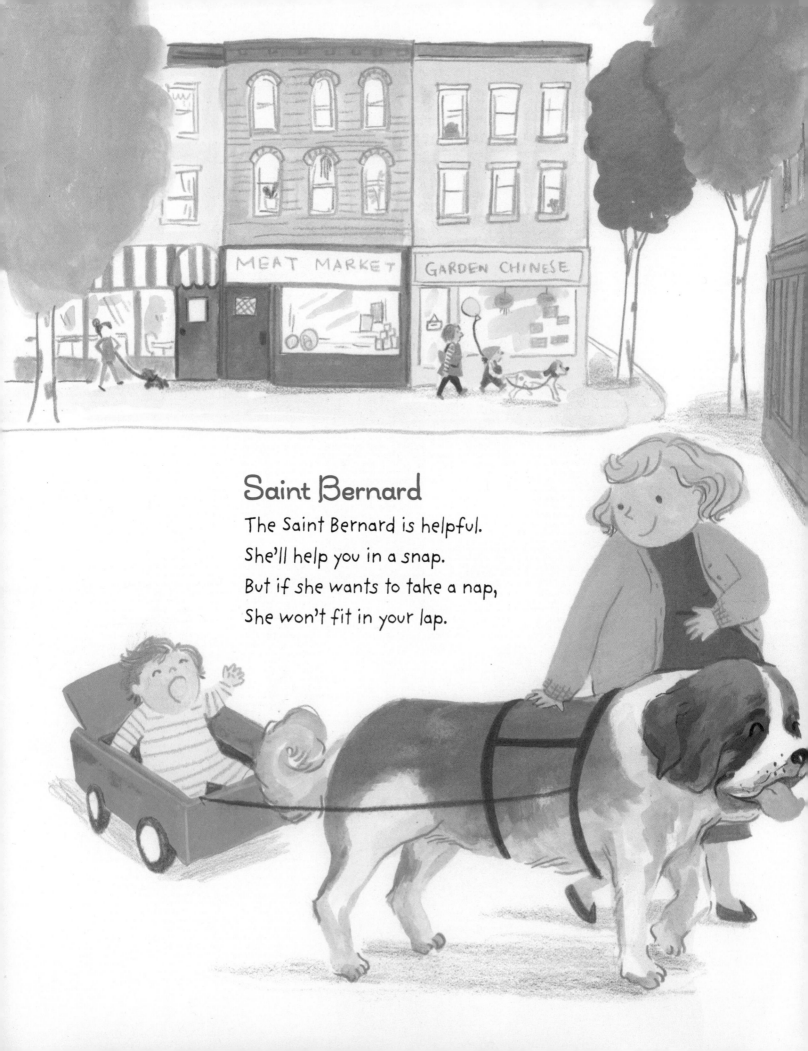

Saint Bernard

The Saint Bernard is helpful.
She'll help you in a snap.
But if she wants to take a nap,
She won't fit in your lap.

Siberian Husky

If dogs have dreams, they must have dreams
Of simple things they know.
If Huskies dream, they must have dreams
Of running in the snow.

Dalmatian

You've got an easy way to spot him.

He has spots on his top and spots on his bottom.

Pointer

She'll stiffen every single joint
And point and point and point
And point.

Standard Schnauzer

The Schnauzer is
A bit of a browser
Who browses for mice,
Which makes him a mouser.

Scottish Terrier

The whiskers and the chunky body
Lets you know that she's a "Scotty."

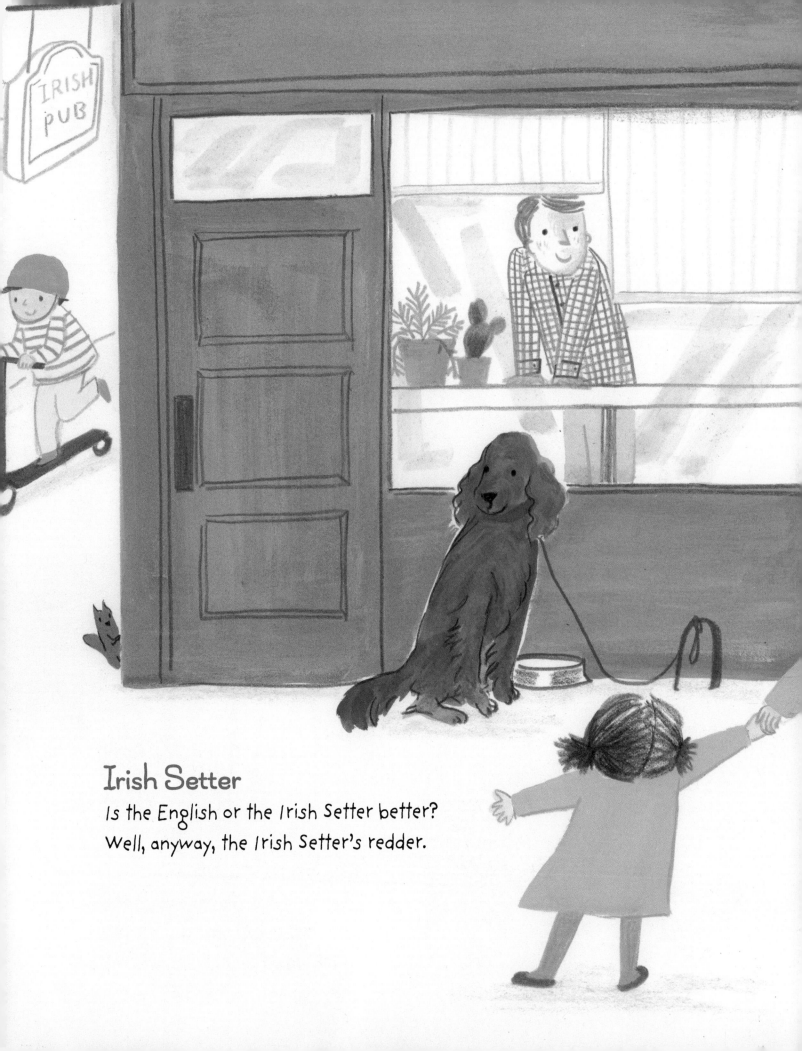

Irish Setter
Is the English or the Irish Setter better?
Well, anyway, the Irish Setter's redder.

Yorkshire Terrier
Like very many little dogs,
His bark is more a yap.
He's often carried in a bag,
Or fits right in your lap.

Lhasa Apso
Lhapsa Aso? No, Lhasa Apso.
Here's our chap, so
You could tell him anywhere
By his special head of hair.

Shih Tzu

She's like a Lhasa Apso
With different hair around her face.
Which of them is cuter?
Either one could win that race.

So here's to dogs both big and little
And the others in the middle.
And here's to all the mixed breeds, too.
Being friends with a dog is a dream come true.

Labrador Retriever

Poodle

Old English Sheepdog

Newfoundland

Lhasa Apso

Irish Setter

Dalmatian

Standard Schnauzer

Siberian Husky

Border Collie

Collie

Pointer

Yorkshire Terrier

Saint Bernard

Shih Tzu

Puli

Greyhound

Saluki

Scottish Terrier